advancing learning, changing lives

Edexcel GCSE
Anthology
of Music

Edited by Julia Winterson

A PEARSON COMPANY

Published by Pearson Education Limited, a company incorporated in England and Wales, having its registered office at Edinburgh Gate, Harlow, Essex, CM20 2JE. Registered company number: 872828

www.heinemann.co.uk
Edexcel is a registered trademark of Edexcel Limited
Text copyright © 2009 Hinrichsen Edition, Peters Edition Limited, London
First published 2009
Second Impression 2009
www.editionpeters.com
British Library Cataloguing in Publication Data is available from the British Library on request.

ISBN 978-1-84690-405-9

Companion 2-CD set available
ISBN 978-1-84690-406-6

Text and music originated by Peter Nickol
Cover design © Pearson Education Limited 2009
Printed in Malaysia, CTP-KHL

Disclaimer
This Edexcel publication offers high-quality support for the delivery of Edexcel qualifications.

Edexcel endorsement does not mean that this material is essential to achieve any Edexcel qualification, nor does it mean that this is the only suitable material available to support any Edexcel qualification. No endorsed material will be used verbatim in setting any Edexcel examination/assessment and any resource lists produced by Edexcel shall include this and other appropriate texts.

Copies of official specifications for all Edexcel qualifications may be found on the Edexcel website: www.edexcel.com

Contents

Acknowledgements

The publishers would like to thank all those who contributed their time and expertise to the development of this anthology, in particular Peter Nickol for his score design and technical expertise through the period of preparation for publication. We are grateful to Barry Russell for his transcriptions of scores (*All blues*, *Grace*, *Why does my heart feel so bad*, *Skye Waulking Song*, and *Yiri*) and to Lewis Riley for his work on Rag Desh. Our thanks are due to Paul Terry for his support and advice.

George Frideric Handel
'And the glory of the Lord' from Messiah

CD1 • track 1

The performance on the CD is by the Scholars Baroque Ensemble. They have recreated the work as first performed in Dublin on 13 April 1742, using a small string band with no oboes or bassoons. Handel expanded the orchestra for later performances.

Wolfgang Amadeus Mozart
Symphony No. 40 in G minor, K550
Movement I

CD1 • track 2

* A horn in B flat alto sounded a major 2nd lower than written. A horn in B flat basso sounded a major 9th lower.

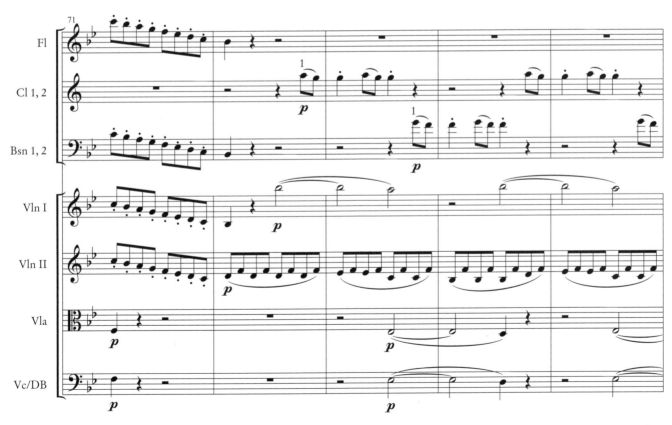

Fryderyk Chopin
Prelude No. 15 in D flat major, Op. 28

CD1 • track 3

Arnold Schoenberg
'Peripetie' from Five Orchestral Pieces

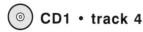 **CD1 • track 4**

This score is 'at concert pitch': all instruments sound as shown, except the piccolo, which sounds an octave higher, and the contrabassoon and double bass, which sound an octave lower.

Leonard Bernstein
'Something's coming' from West Side Story

◎ **CD1** • **track 5**

Steve Reich
Electric Counterpoint (movement III)

 CD1 • track 6

This piece is for solo guitar with a taped or live guitar ensemble (seven guitars in this movement) and two bass guitars.

At the head of the score, the composer provides this performance note:

When *Electric Counterpoint* is performed with soloist and pre-recorded tape the soloist should be amplified so that his or her volume and timbre will fit properly with the tape. The soloist may play either electric or acoustic guitar. If electric the amplification is done directly from the output of the instrument; if acoustic a conventional microphone is used placed as close as possible to the instrument. Basically the soloist should always be somewhat louder than the tape but not so loud that the relationship between soloist and tape is lost. An assistant who knows the proper balance between soloist and tape (either from hearing a properly balanced previous performance or reliable recording) should sit at the mixer in a good listening position in the hall and adjust the volume of the soloist vis a vis the tape as necessary throughout the performance. Though the rental tape is stereo the soloist and the assistant may decide to play it back in mono in the hall so that all members of the audience get a good overall balance regardless of where they are sitting. In my experience, using a well recorded cassette (with noise reduction) and a small portable professional quality cassette recorder for playback works quite well. It is wise to use a recorder that has a playback speed adjustment so that the pitch of the tape can be slightly adjusted if necessary. Whatever the adjustment in speed made it should be done in rehearsal and then not touched in performance.

Generally a monitor speaker (usually wedge shaped) should be placed on the floor directly next to the soloist so that he or she can hear the tape clearly throughout the performance. A sound check rehearsal is necessary in each different hall to determine the tape/soloist balance for the house, for the monitor, and for the exact placement of house and monitor speakers. A performance diagram follows:

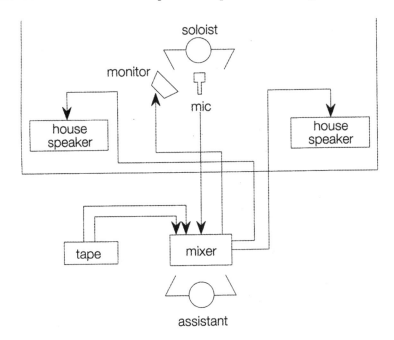

If a performer wishes to make their own pre-recorded tape they are encouraged to do so and will need to record it in a multi-track tape studio. Generally at least 16 tracks are necessary to allow for alternate takes during the recording sessions. The multi-track tape is then mixed down to a 2 track stereo (or mono) tape for performance.

Steve Reich

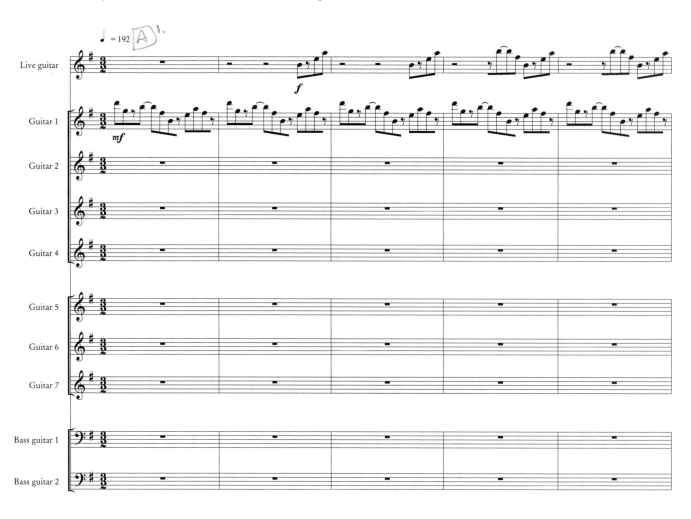

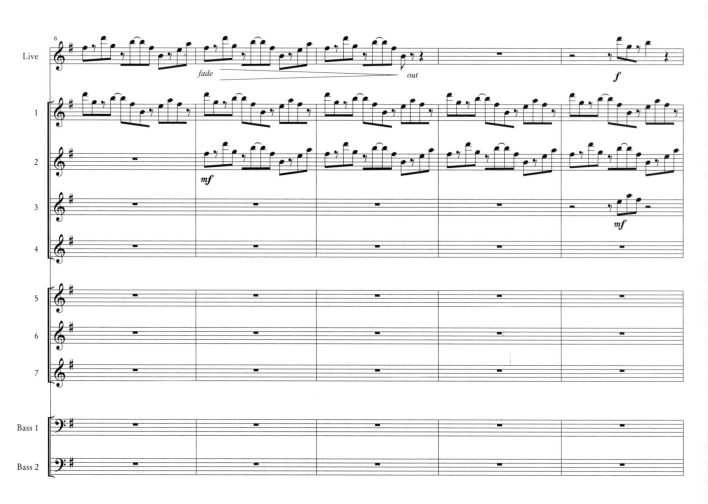

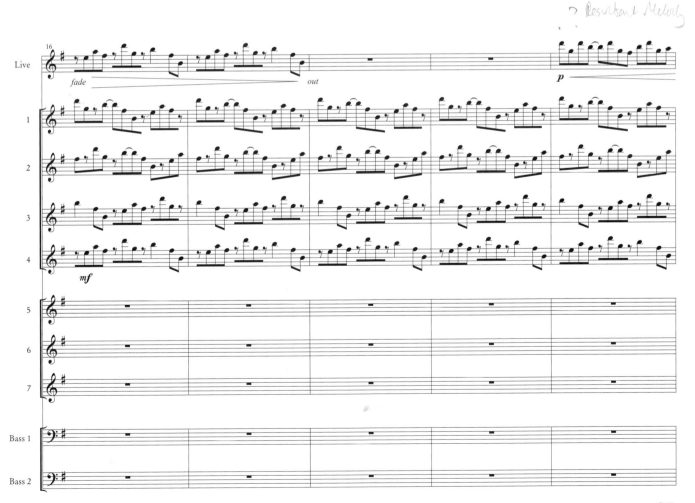

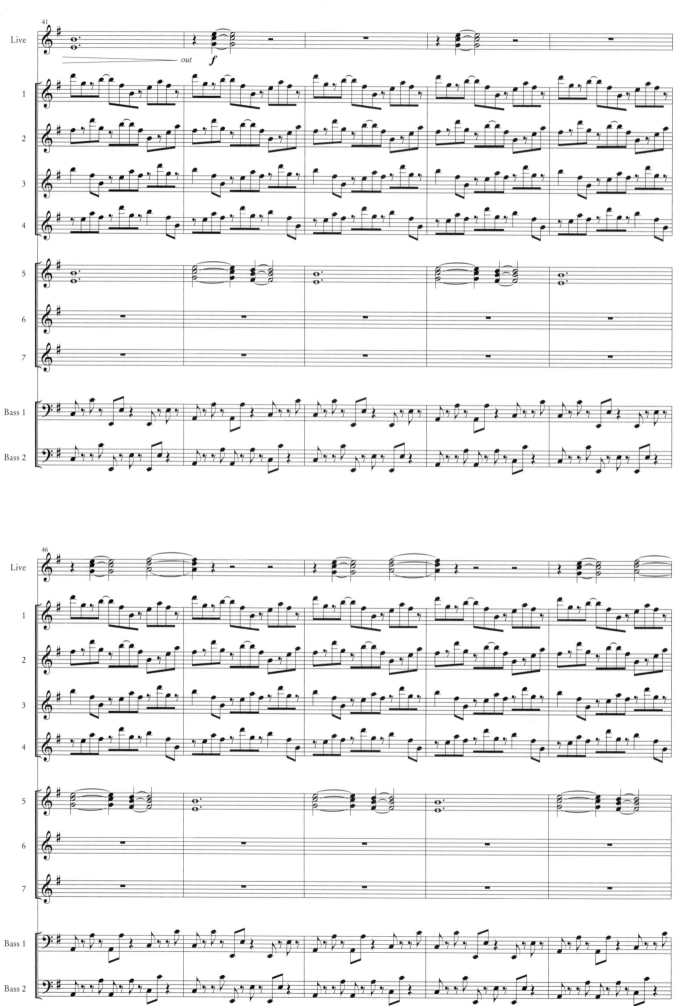

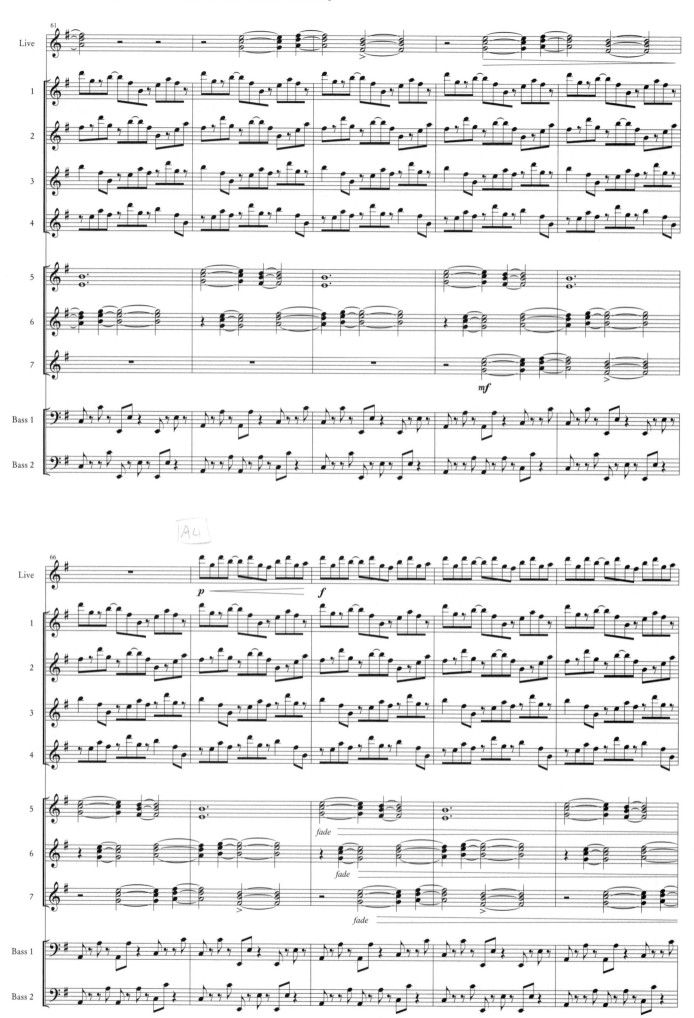

coda 9

All blues
as recorded by Miles Davis

 CD2 • track 1

'All blues' is in 12-bar blues form. It was included on the *Kind of Blue* album by Miles Davis, released in 1959. In addition to the soloists listed below, the players were Paul Chambers (bass) and Jimmy Cobb (drums).

00:00	bar 1	Introductory 4 bars	05:34	129	Alto sax solo 4
00:11	5	Main intro riff (4 bars), played on saxes in 3rds.	06:04	141	Intro riff (piano)
			06:15	145	Tenor sax solo 1 (John Coltrane)
00:21	9	Head 1, muted trumpet (Miles Davis) – 12 bars	06:45	157	Tenor sax solo 2
			07:16	169	Tenor sax solo 3
00:53	21	Intro riff	07:46	181	Tenor sax solo 4
01:03	25	Head 2	08:17	193	Intro riff
01:35	37	Intro riff	08:27	197	Piano solo 1 (Bill Evans)
01:46	41	Trumpet solo 1 (unmuted until return at 09:38)	08:57	209	Piano solo 2
			09:28	221	Intro riff (saxes)
02:17	53	Trumpet solo 2	09:38	225	Head 3, muted trumpet
02:49	65	Trumpet solo 3	10:09	237	Intro riff
03:20	77	Trumpet solo 4	10:20	241	Head 4
03:51	89	Intro riff on piano	10:51	253	Intro riff
04:01	93	Alto sax solo 1 (Cannonball Adderley)	11:01	257	Coda: trumpet solo 5 (still muted)
04:32	105	Alto sax solo 2	11:33		fades
05:03	117	Alto sax solo 3			

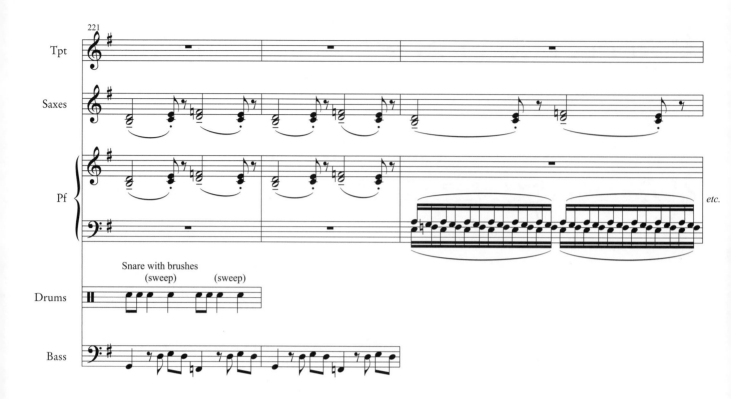

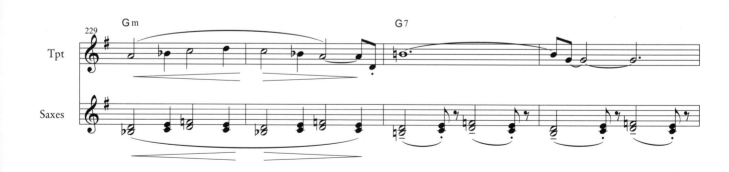

Grace
as recorded by Jeff Buckley

CD2 • track 2

Why does my heart feel so bad?
as recorded by Moby

◉ **CD2 • track 3**

The album *Play* was recorded and mixed at Moby's home studio. Equipment used: (piano sounds with SPX900 reverb) Emu Proformance piano module, Yamaha synth; Akai 3200 sampler; Roland TR909 drum machine; (string sounds) Yamaha SY22 and SY85 synths; and (sub-bass line) Roland Juno 106 synth.

In 'Why does my heart feel so bad', each **A** section is 8 bars long, and each has the same chord sequence:
    Am Em G D.
Each **B** section is likewise 8 bars long, but **B** sections are of two types:
    Bx uses the chord sequence C Am C Am (each chord for two bars).
    By uses the chord sequence F C F C.

A1
0:00
Piano only, establishing the main chord sequence

A2
0:19
Adds male voice (sample taken from a recording of a 1953 gospel choir)

A3
0:39
Adds percussion (Roland TR909 plus sampled hip-hop breakbeat) and countermelody

A4
0:59

Adds bass and string-synth (Yamaha SY22 and SY85) chords

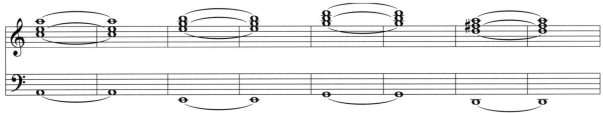

A5
1:19

More syncopated version of piano chords

etc.

Bx1
1:38

Female voice takes over from male voice, with a two-bar phrase which is then repeated throughout the B sections. New chord sequence.

These ___ o-pen doors ___   These ___ o-pen doors ___

By1
1:57

Voice continues with the same two-bar phrase, sometimes with added echo-canons and shouts. New chord sequence: F F C C F F C C.

A6
2:17

The male voice resumes as before. A second vocal line is used in 'question and answer' style. The part was treated to some delay and heavy EQ during the mix.

A7
2:37

Repeats **A6**.

2:56

One bar's pause, with fading echoes, followed by…

Bx2
2:59

The female voice resumes, distant, repeating the two-bar phrase as before, but this time accompanied by static chords, no piano or percussion.

By2
3:18

Change of chord sequence as before. Piano and percussion resume, and the female voice comes back to the foreground. Echo-canons and shouts as in **By1**.

By3
3:38

Repeats **By2**.

A8
3:57

Male voice resumes, but accompanied by static chords, no piano or percussion.

Chuir m'athair mise dhan taigh charraideach
(the Skye Waulking Song)
as recorded by Capercaillie

 CD2 • track 4

The Skye Waulking Song is a Gaelic folksong arranged by Capercaillie.

'Chuir m'athair mise dhan taigh charraideach' (My father sent me to the house of sorrow) is an excerpt taken from the lament 'Seathan, Mac Righ Eirann' (Seathan, Son of the King of Ireland). It is taken from a large collection of Gaelic folksongs assembled by the folklorist Alexander Carmichael. A waulking song is a work song, sung by women workers processing cloth.

Hi ri huraibhi o ho

Chuir m'athair mise dhan taigh charraideach   My father sent me to the house of sorrow

O hi a bho ro hu o ho

'N oidhche sin a rinn e bhanais dhomh	That night he held my wedding for me
Gur truagh a Righ nach b'e m'fhalairidh	What a pity, O King, that it wasn't my funeral party
Man do bhrist mo làmh an t-aran dhomh	Before my hand broke the bread for me
Man d'rinn mo sgian biadh a ghearradh dhomh	Before my knife cut the food for me
Sheathain chridhe nan sùl socair	Beloved Seathan of the calm eyes
Tha do bhàta 'nochd 's na portaibh	Your boat tonight is in port,
Och, ma tha, chan eil i socair	Oh, if it is, it won't be calm
O nach robh thu, ghaoil, na toiseach.	Oh that you weren't, my love, in her bow.

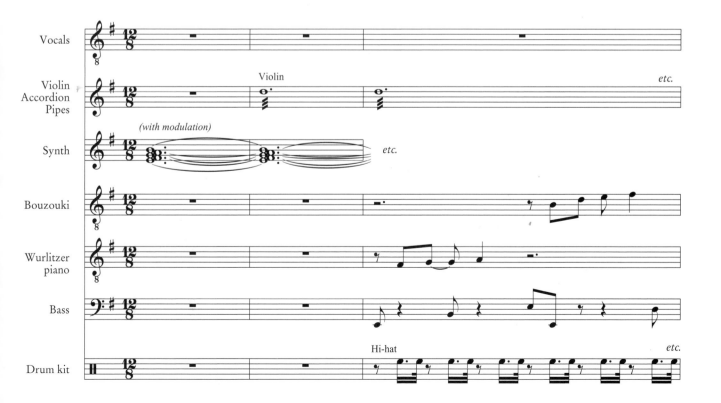

Hi ri hu-rai-bhi— o ho Man d'rinn mo sgi-an—— biadh a ghea-rradh dhomh——

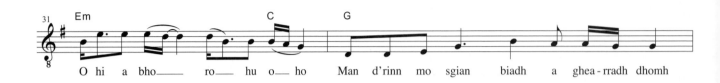

O hi a bho—— ro— hu o— ho Man d'rinn mo sgian biadh a ghea-rradh dhomh

Hi ri—— hu-rai-bhi— o ho Shea-thain—— chridhe nan sùl so-cair—— O hi a bho—— ro— hu o— ho

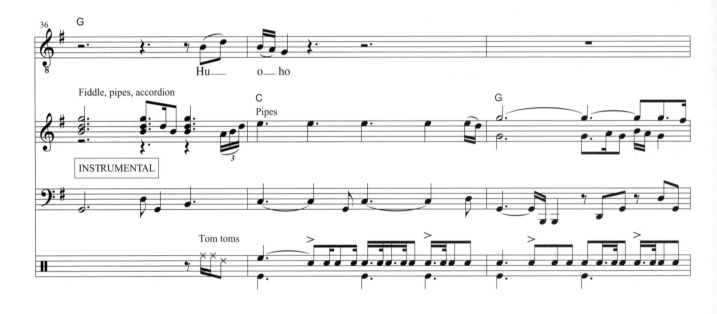

Hu— o— ho

INSTRUMENTAL

Rag Desh
as recorded by Anoushka Shankar; Chiranji Lal Tanwar; and Benjy Wertheimer and Steve Gorn

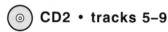 CD2 • tracks 5–9

The examples of classical Indian music here are all from the North Indian (Hindustani) tradition. The older South Indian (Carnatic) tradition has similarities, but also many differences, and is regarded as a separate style of playing and singing.

Most Indian music is based on three elements – melody, rhythm and drone. The melodic lines are all based on patterns of notes known as **rags** (pronounced with a long 'a': 'raags'). A rag isn't quite like a Western scale: it is characterised by particular phrases, or emphases on particular notes, and there may be different combinations of notes ascending or descending. Rags are traditionally played at particular times of the day (or night), and some are also associated with the seasons. Rag Desh is a late evening rag associated with the monsoon season. It is considered to be a lighter rag with its origins in *thumri* (courtly love songs), and is often performed at a medium fast tempo.

The example below shows the notes used in Rag Desh, beginning on C. In Indian music a system known as *sargam* is used for naming the notes: Sa, Re, Ga, Ma, Pa, Dha, Ni, Sa. (It is comparable with the Western sol-fa system.) The tonic, or ground note, is Sa – this is heard in the drone. Pa and Re are other important notes in Rag Desh.

Rhythms are usually in cycles of beats called **tals** (or talas). The most common are 6, 7, 8, 10, 12 or 16 beats long, grouped in units of two, three or four beats. It is common to mark tal by handclaps and waves – clapping on strong beats and waving on the weak (or empty) beats. The first beat of a cycle is known as *sam*. The most common tal is *tintal*:

Tintal (16 beats): 4 + 4 + 4 + 4

1	2	3	4	5	6	7	8	9	10	11	12	13	14	15	16
clap				clap				wave				clap			

The **tabla** is the percussion instrument most often found in Hindustani music. It consists of a pair of drums placed side by side on the floor in front of the player. One (the *dayan*, meaning 'right') is tuned to Sa, the tonic note of the rag, and is quite high in pitch, whilst the other (*bayan* – 'left') is deeper in pitch and provides a bass sound. They are played with the fingers of each hand and, on the bayan, the heel of the hand is pressed into the drum to change the pitch, providing a distinctive sound.

The **drone** is the sound usually heard first, stating the tonic note, Sa. The drone is often played these days by an electronic box, but is more traditionally played on a **tanpura**, a stringed instrument that looks rather like a sitar but has no frets and only 4–6 (usually 4) strings.

Rag Desh as performed by Anoushka Shankar (sitar)

In this live recording Anoushka Shankar plays the **sitar** – a long-necked plucked string instrument with movable frets, a hollow body and a gourd resonator. The number of strings is not standardised but there are usually 6 or 7 main strings, which are plucked, and 12 or more sympathetic strings running beneath them. These resonate in sympathy, adding to the characteristic shimmering sound. Notes can be bent up by pulling the strings to the side.

Two tals are used in this performance: *tintal* (see previous page) and *jhaptal*:

Jhaptal (10 beats): 2 + 3 + 2 + 3

1	2	3	4	5	6	7	8	9	10
clap		clap			wave		clap		

0:00	The performance opens with a short improvised **alap** – a slow, introductory section where the unaccompanied sitar introduces the notes and the mood of the rag. The rhythm is free and there is no regular pulse. Note the intricate decoration to the melodic line made by pulling the strings to get from one note to another rather than just using the frets.
0:55	Here the **gat** is introduced: a fixed composition which is often varied by adding improvised decoration. It is played at *madhyalaya*, meaning medium speed.
0:58	The tabla enters in *jhaptal*, with improvisation and decoration around the basic beats. Tabla and sitar alternate short melodic and rhythmic improvisations. The ending of these improvisations is shown by playing a **tihai**, a rhythmic and melodic device where a short phrase is played three times, often across the beat, before it lands on *sam*, the first beat of the cycle. These *tihais* of various lengths can be heard at: 3:01–3:03, 3:11–3:19, 3:27–3:34 and 3:40–3:50.
3:55	The sitar improvises, using triplet phrasing called *chand*. The section again ends in a *tihai*.
5:02	Improvisations continue, now with four notes to each beat. Sitar and tabla alternate, using a *tihai* to signal the end of each solo spot.
9:27	The final section is a *drut* (fast) *gat* in *tintal*.
10:10	The drone strings (*chikari*) of the sitar are strummed to give added rhythmic effect called **jhalla**. A final *tihai* is played, starting at 11:11, to end the piece.

'Mhara janam maran', in Rag Desh, performed by Chiranji Lal Tanwar (voice)

This type of song is known as a **bhajan**, a Hindu devotional song from Rajasthan. The words are by Mira Bai, a Rajput princess and India's best known saint-poetess. In the song she is pining at night for the Hindu deity Lord Krishna, her partner in life and death, to arrive in the morning.

> *Mhara janam maran rasaathi thane nahin bisru din raati*
>> You are my companion through life and death and I cannot forget you night and day
> *tha dekhiyan bin kal nahinaave jaane mhari chhati*
>> My heart pines for you and I feel totally restless when I am not able to see you.

The ensemble includes **sarod**, **sarangi**, **pakhawaj**, **cymbals** and **tabla**, as well as the featured solo singer. The **sarod** is another plucked string intrument with main and sympathetic strings. It is made of wood but is shorter than the sitar and has no frets. It is plucked with a wooden plectrum and has a smooth metal fingerboard. The bending of notes is achieved by sliding along the fingerboard.

The **sarangi** is a fretless bowed intrument. It is held in the lap, and has three thick strings and as many as 36 sympathetic strings. The pitch is changed by pushing the base of the left hand fingernails against the string and sliding up and down – a painful technique to learn.

The **pakhawaj** is a large double-headed drum played with both hands.

The tal used in this performance is *keherwa tal*:

Keherwa tal (8 beats): 2 + 2 + 2 + 2

1	2	3	4	5	6	7	8
clap		clap		wave		clap	

NB These beats are the equivalent of a quaver in the following music example.

0:00   A short *alap* is heard, first on sarangi and then voice, which sings a version of the song's 'chorus':

0:50   The first line of the song is sung again, but in tempo in *keherwatal*, with the tabla joining in.

1:10   A short sarod interlude

1:22   Sarangi solo

Subsequent verses are then sung at 1:32, 3:04 and 4:50, returning to the first line as a kind of 'chorus' after which sarangi and sarod again perform short improvised solos. This pattern continues until the piece ends in a short *tihai*.

Rag Desh performed by Steve Gorn (bansuri) and Benjy Wertheimer (esraj and tabla)

The **bansuri** is a bamboo flute, with no keys but simple holes over which the fingers are placed. The notes are bent by gradually covering or uncovering the holes. The **esraj** is a bowed string instrument, played sitting on the floor like the **sarangi**, but with frets like a sitar. It also has a number of sympathetic and drone strings.

Part 1 – Alap (track 7)

0:00–8:35   The drone provides the notes Sa and Pa (tonic and 5th), which in this case correspond to the notes D and A in concert pitch. A zither can be heard occasionally in the background, gently strumming the notes of the rag. The alap introduces the notes and the mood of the rag, and shows characteristic phrases and decoration associated with Rag Desh. Note the use of both natural and sharp 7ths (C and C♯).

Part 2 – Slow gat in *rupak tal* (track 8)

Rupak tal (7 beats): 3 + 2 + 2

1	2	3	4	5	6	7
wave			clap		clap	

0:00   A short unaccompanied flute solo leads into an opening flourish from the tabla (starting 0:31) which introduces the first beat of rupak tal, and the composed *gat* (starting 0:43). The words below the notes are not sung; they are *bols*, or rhythm words marking the tal and indicating different types and strengths of beat.

tin   tin   na   dhin   na——— dhin—— na——   tin   tin   na   dhin—— na— dhin— na

1:02   There follows a section of flute improvisation around the *gat*, whilst the tabla keeps the tal with many embellishments.

3:06   The flute now plays the *gat* over and over whilst the tabla player improvises around the tal.

3:32   Again roles of improviser and accompanist are reversed as the flute takes over and the tabla keeps the tal. Towards the end a couple of *tihais* are heard, one at 4:19–4:24 and a final one at 4:32–4:41. This leads directly into:

Part 3 – fast (*drut*) gat in *ektal* (track 9)

Ektal (12 beats): 2 + 2 + 2 + 2 + 2 + 2

1	2	3	4	5	6	7	8	9	10	11	12
clap		clap		wave		clap		wave		clap	

The tabla introduces this final section with a *tihai* leading into fast *ektal*, the *sam* being at 0:10. The tabla player plays the tal at a speed of 2 beats = 120. The flute plays a *drut* gat. The fast improvised scale passages are known as **tans**. A final *chakkradar tihai*, a three-times-three repetition of phrases, starts at 2:31.

Yiri
as recorded by Koko

 CD2 • track 10

Large talking drum, small talking drum and djembe
Resultant rhythm:

Copyright acknowledgements

Index